Collins COBUILD

Phrasal Verbs
Workbook

THE UNIVERSITY
OF BIRMINGHAM

COLLINS
COBUILD

HarperCollins*Publishers*

second edition 2002

© **HarperCollins Publishers 1993, 2002**

HarperCollins Publishers
Westerhill Road, Bishopbriggs, Glasgow G64 2QT,
Great Britain

www.cobuild.collins.co.uk

Collins®, COBUILD®, and Bank of English® are registered
trademarks of HarperCollins Publishers Limited

ISBN 0-00-713178-X

Corpus Acknowledgements

We would like to acknowledge the assistance of the many
hundreds of individuals and companies who have kindly given
permission for copyright material to be used in the Bank of
English. The written sources include many national and regional
newspapers in Britain and overseas; magazine and periodical
publishers; and book publishers in Britain, the United States and
Australia. Extensive spoken data have been provided by radio
and television broadcasting companies; research workers
at many universities and other institutions; and numerous
individual contributors. We are grateful to them all.

Author Acknowledgement

We would like to thank the author of the first edition of the
COBUILD Phrasal Verbs Workbook, Malcolm Goodale, for his work in
creating the original text, on which we have based this edition.

Note

Entered words that we have reason to believe constitute
trademarks have been designated as such. However, neither the
presence nor absence of such designation should be regarded
as affecting the legal status of any trademark.

Typeset by Rosetta Publishing, Peebles

Printed and bound in Great Britain by Montgomery Litho Group

Contents

Introduction

This workbook has been written to accompany the **Collins COBUILD Dictionary of Phrasal Verbs**. The workbook can be used on its own, but further benefit will be gained by working closely with the dictionary.

The **Collins COBUILD Phrasal Verbs Workbook** is divided up into units, and each unit provides practice in individual particles. This workbook practises the most important phrasal verbs, which have over 150 different meanings. Six very common verbs – *bring*, *come*, *get*, *go*, *put* and *take* – account for many of the phrasal verbs in this workbook.

The workbook is a vocabulary book rather than a grammar book. The examples and exercises throughout the book show the different syntactic patterns of the phrasal verbs. The most important phrasal verbs, and also the ones that are most difficult for learners, are the adverbial phrasal verbs, for example, *turn down*. For this reason, prepositional phrasal verbs such as *rely on* are not included in this workbook.

For more detailed information about phrasal verbs and also their grammar, please refer to the **Collins COBUILD Dictionary of Phrasal Verbs**, as well as the **Collins COBUILD English Grammar**.

How to use this workbook

There are 10 units of material. The first 9 units deal with single particles and these units are arranged in alphabetical order in the book; the final unit concentrates on 7 more particles. The particle of the phrasal verb can often give you important information about the meaning, which can help you to understand new phrasal verbs. All the units follow a similar format, and can be studied in any order. As this book is designed for both classwork and self-study, a full answer key to the exercises is given at the back of the book.

At the beginning of each unit there is a section which gives the important meanings of the particle being studied, with lists of the phrasal verbs to be studied in each section of the unit. Sometimes a phrasal verb appears twice in the same section, with two meanings. Quite often, a phrasal verb appears in 2 or more different sections. This is not surprising, as many phrasal verbs have more than one meaning, and some have as many as 20 different meanings!

The final section of some units is called *Other Meanings*. This includes phrasal verbs which often do fit into a category of meaning, but the category is too small or limited to be included separately. You will find more information about these categories in the Particles Index of the dictionary.

The sections

Each section of a unit covers one category of meaning. Each section begins with a list of the verbs included and example sentences, showing how each verb is typically used. All the sentences are taken from the *Bank of English*, our 450 million-word database of spoken and written English, and have been thoroughly updated for this second edition. All the exercises also use examples from the *Bank of English*, so you can be sure that you are practising phrasal verbs as they are really used in spoken and written English. The examples are often followed by a Language Comment section, which highlights other phrasal verbs with similar meanings, and also gives synonyms if these exist. It is a common misconception that phrasal verbs are mostly used in spoken English. They can be found in many styles of writing, including highly formal government reports, and the range of examples reflects these different contexts.

The exercises

The first exercise in each section of the unit asks you to complete the definitions of all the phrasal verbs in the section. In this way, you can build up a record of the most important phrasal verbs for future reference. Subsequent exercises involve matching phrases or sentences and completing gapped sentences. In completing gapped sentences, you should pay particular attention to the form of the verb. The final exercise in each unit asks you to write a paragraph on one of three given topics. Many learners are able to understand phrasal verbs in reading texts, but have difficulty using them accurately in their own spoken and written English. This final exercise helps you to develop this skill by producing your own texts including some of the phrasal verbs you have studied in the unit.

Recording new phrasal verbs

At the end of each unit there is a table where you can record new phrasal verbs you find in your studies and reading, with space to include a definition and an example sentence. It is a very good idea when studying phrasal verbs to keep a note of the sentence in which you find the verb, as the context will give you important information about the meaning of the verb and how it should be used. The tables at the end of each unit will help you to do this effectively, by categorizing the verbs according to the meaning of the particles.

In this way, as well as providing practice of phrasal verbs, this workbook also helps you to build up a comprehensive record of the most important phrasal verbs in English and their meanings.

We hope that you will enjoy using the **Collins COBUILD Phrasal Verbs Workbook**. We always welcome comments from learners and students, and you can contact us on our website at: http://www.cobuild.collins.co.uk
by email directly to: cobuild@ref.collins.co.uk
or you can write to us at the following address:

Collins COBUILD
Westerhill Road
Bishopbriggs
Glasgow G64 2QT
UK

Shown below is the most important meaning of 'away' and one group of other meanings.

Under each of the headings you will see a list of the phrasal verbs which you are going to practise in the exercises given in this unit. Some verbs appear more than once, because many phrasal verbs have more than one meaning.

Withdrawing and separating

get away

give away

keep away

run away

take away

Other meanings

fade away

throw away

get away with

hide away

put away

write away

You can write other phrasal verbs with 'away' with related meanings in the space provided at the end of this unit. You can use a dictionary to help you.

Withdrawing and separating

get away   **give away**   **keep away**   **run away**   **take away**

His father had thought it would be good for his character to <u>get away</u> from home and earn some money on his own.

I could not decide whether to keep the money he left me or <u>give</u> it <u>away</u>.

It would be better to <u>keep away</u> and not attempt to enter the city until she knew what was happening there.

I <u>ran away</u> from my mother and she ran after me and coaxed me to come back.

They took my name and address, <u>took away</u> all my possessions, and sent me down to the cells.

A   *Using your understanding of the examples above, write the correct phrasal verb to complete the definitions. Be careful with verb forms.*

1   If you _____ _____, you move quickly and farther from a place or person, or leave secretly because you are unhappy.

2   If you _____ something _____ from a place or position, you remove it and put it somewhere else. If you _____ something _____ from a person, you remove it and prevent them from having it any more.

3   If you _____ _____ from a place or a person, you succeed in leaving or escaping.

4   If you _____ _____ from a place, you avoid going there.

5   If you _____ something _____, you give it to someone without taking money in return.

B   *Match the phrases on the left with those on the right.*

1   I had to **get away**.
2   I think of the new boy who **ran away**
3   She has **given away** jewellery
4   The more you **keep away** from the shops,
5   These men wanted to help them keep their land,

a   the less money you'll spend.
b   worth millions of pounds.
c   not **take** it **away** from them.
d   One way or another, I was going to leave Birmingham.
e   because he was being bullied.

1	2	3	4	5

C   *Write the correct form of the appropriate phrasal verb in the space provided.*

1   You should always _____ animals _____ from the kitchen.

2   The plan was to _____ 30 million telephone directories.

3   She let herself out and raced down the stairs and _____ along the road.

4   Let's go out for a walk to _____ from it all.

5   She had _____ the children _____ with her to her parents' house.

Other meanings

fade away   **throw away**   **get away with**   **hide away**   **put away**

The sun's warmth began to <u>fade away</u>.

30 million tonnes of refuse are <u>thrown away</u> in the UK.

I'm not going to allow Anne to <u>get away with</u> an offensive remark like that.

He looked at his drawings of the rocks and <u>hid</u> them <u>away</u> again.

Hamish began to <u>put away</u> a vast load of shopping he had brought home.

A *Using your understanding of the examples above, write the correct phrasal verb to complete the definitions. Be careful with verb forms.*

1   If you _____ something _____, you put it in a place where nobody else can find it.

2   If something _____ _____, it slowly becomes less intense, frequent, or common, until it ends or disappears completely.

3   If you _____ something _____, you place it tidily somewhere, for example in a cupboard, drawer, or pocket.

4   If you _____ _____ _____ something that you should not have done, you are not criticized or punished for it.

5   If you _____ _____ something that you no longer need, you get rid of it, for example by putting it in a dustbin.

B *Match the phrases on the left with those on the right.*

1   Her new-found enthusiasm for running   a   rather than **throw** them **away**

2   You see, I may need somewhere   b   on the nose and **got away with** it.

3   He had punched a teacher   c   will soon **fade away**.

4   We cleared up in silence, Lally   d   to **hide away** for a week or two.
    washing up,   e   the two of us drying up

5   She likes to keep things, even old things,   and **putting away**.

1	2	3	4	5

C *Write the correct form of the appropriate phrasal verb in the space provided.*

1   I had to _____ the presents in the bedroom, so that the children wouldn't find them.

2   He could make the most outrageous statements and somehow _____ it.

3   The music and laughter graduallly _____ as the procession moved off down the street.

4   _____ medicine after an illness. It's unlikely you'll use it again.

5   Albert folded the newspaper neatly and _____ it _____.

Consolidation

Write a paragraph on one of the following topics, including at least four of the phrasal verbs you have studied in this unit.

a   The diamond theft.

b   Escape!

c   The end of the romance.

Use the space below to record other phrasal verbs with 'away' you find in your studies. Write down the meaning in the second column and keep a note of the sentence in which you find the verb in the third column. An example is given.

AWAY – WITHDRAWING AND SEPARATING		

AWAY – OTHER MEANINGS		
do away with	If you <u>do away with</u> something, you get rid of it or abolish it.	The goal must be to <u>do away with</u> nuclear weapons.

Shown below are the two most important meanings of 'back'. Under each of the headings you will see a list of the phrasal verbs which you are going to practise in the exercises given in this unit.

Returning or repeating

call back

get back

give back

take back

Controlling or suppressing

cut back on

fight back

set back

You can write other phrasal verbs with 'back' with related meanings in the space provided at the end of this unit. You can use a dictionary to help you.

Returning or repeating

call back   get back   give back   take back

Pitts _called back_[1] on Thursday, saying he hadn't been able to make the arrangements.

I left early yesterday and didn't _get back_ till late. I had to go up to London to see my lawyer.

She wants to _give_ them _back_ a pride in their appearance.

We're going to _take_ the typewriter _back_ to the shop.

LANGUAGE COMMENT

[1] **Phone back** and **ring back** mean almost the same as **call back**, but **call back** can also mean to visit a place again.

A   _Using your understanding of the examples above, write the correct phrasal verb to complete the definitions. Be careful with verb forms._

1   If you _____ _____ something which you borrowed or bought, you return it to the place or person that you got it from, for example because you have finished using it, or because it is damaged.

2   If you _____ someone_____, you telephone someone who has contacted you previously, or telephone them again.

3   If you _____ something _____, you return it to the person who gave it to you or to whom it belongs.

4   If you _____ _____ to a place or position, you return there after you have been somewhere else.

B   _Match the phrases on the left with those on the right._

1	They were totally useless,	a He will **call** you **back** later.
2	The symptoms disappeared	b I would **give** it **back** again.
3	If I didn't need the money,	c but we wouldn't **take** them **back**.
4	I'm sorry, Mr Smith is out.	d and he was able to **get back** to work.

1	2	3	4

C   *Write the correct form of the appropriate phrasal verb in the space provided.*

1   Don't forget to _____ your books _____ to the library.

2   Don't you think we'd better _____ to the subject?

3   I shall make some enquiries and _____ you _____.

4   I _____ her _____ her newspaper.

Controlling or suppressing

cut back on   fight back   set back

I did eliminate egg yolks and <u>cut back</u>[1] a bit <u>on</u> red meats. But I still enjoy eating out.

If we did that, importing countries could <u>fight back</u>[2] with laws of their own.

This has <u>set back</u>[3] the whole programme of nuclear power in America.

LANGUAGE COMMENT

[1] **Reduce** and **resist** are more formal words for **cut back on**.
There is also a noun: *...the <u>cutback</u> in public services...*
[2] **Retaliate** and **resist** are more formal words for **fight back**.
[3] **Delay** is a more formal word for **set back**, and **hold up** means almost the same.
There is also a noun: *The Union suffered a serious <u>setback</u>.*

A   *Using your understanding of the examples above, write the correct phrasal verb to complete the definitions. Be careful with verb forms.*

1   If you _____ _____ ____ something, such as expenditure, you try to reduce it, often because you can no longer afford it.

2   If something _____ you _____, or _____ _____ your plans, it causes a delay and makes you wait before you can continue with what you want to do.

3   If you _____ _____ when someone attacks you or causes you problems, you defend yourself and try to beat them or stop them.

B   *Match the phrases on the left with those on the right.*

1	When you **cut back on** dairy products,	a have given the disease a chance to **fight back**.
2	The unusual cold of the early spring	b had **set** them **back** with the painting.
3	But collapsing public health systems and increasing poverty	c you **cut back on** cholesterol.

1	2	3

C   *Write the correct form of the appropriate phrasal verb in the space provided.*

1   Bad weather _____ us _____ by about three weeks.

2   Other countries have _____ high-priced Mexican oil.

3   If someone hits you, you have to _____.

Consolidation

Write a paragraph on one of the following topics, including at least three examples of the phrasal verbs you have studied in this unit.

a   The gift.

b   Shopping.

c   The phone call.

More verbs with 'back'

Use the tables below to record other phrasal verbs with 'back' you find. Write down the meaning in the second column and keep a note of the sentence in which you find the verb in the third column. An example is given.

BACK – RETURNING OR REPEATING		
fall back on	If you <u>fall back on</u> something you know you can rely on, you use it or do it when other things have failed.	We have written a script to <u>fall back on</u> if we run out of things to discuss.

BACK – CONTROLLING OR SUPPRESSING		

BACK – OTHER MEANINGS		

11

Shown below are the four most important meanings of 'down'.

Under each of the headings you will see a list of the phrasal verbs which you are going to practise in the exercises given in this unit. Some verbs appear more than once, because many phrasal verbs have more than one meaning.

Decreasing and reducing

bring down
calm down
come down
cut down
play down
slow down

Defeating and suppressing

back down
knock down
pull down
put down

Completing or failing

break down
close down
let down
settle down
turn down

Writing and recording

lay down
put down to
take down

You can write other phrasal verbs with 'down' with related meanings in the space provided at the end of this unit. You can use a dictionary to help you.

Decreasing and reducing

bring down   **calm down**   **come down**   **cut down**   **play down**   **slow down**

The promised measures included steps to <u>bring down</u> prices.

'Please, Mrs Kinter,' said Brody. '<u>Calm down</u>[1]. Let me explain.'

Get on the phone at once, please, and offer to <u>come down</u>[2] a couple of hundred dollars.

Save time for yourself by <u>cutting</u> your shopping <u>down</u> to twice a week.

The Minister tried to <u>play down</u>[3] the seriousness of the problem.

Economic growth has <u>slowed down</u>[4] dramatically.

> **LANGUAGE COMMENT**
>
> [1] **Settle down** means almost the same as **calm down**.
> [2] **Decrease** is a more formal word for **come down**, and **go up** means the opposite.
> [3] **Exaggerate** and **play up** mean the opposite of **play down**.
> [4] **Slow up** means almost the same as **slow down**, and **speed up** means the opposite.

A *Using your understanding of the examples above, write the correct phrasal verb to complete the following definitions. Be careful with verb forms.*

1   If something _____ _____, it becomes much quieter or less intense.

2   If you _____ something _____, you try to make people think that something is unimportant, or less important than it really is.

3   If you _____ something _____, you reduce it or do it less often.

4   If the cost, level or amount of something _____ _____, it becomes cheaper or less than it was before.

5   To _____ _____ the level of something means to reduce it.

6   If something _____ _____ or if you _____ it _____ , it starts to move or happen more slowly.

B *Match the phrases on the left with those on the right.*

1   She said Britain had to save more and borrow less

2   Many smokers who are chemically addicted to nicotine

3   An officer tried to **calm** them **down**

4   Inflation has **come down** this year

5   We did not stop his southward advance

6   He will **play down**

a   the financial difficulties of the company.

b   cannot **cut down** easily.

c   but had no success.

d   to help **bring down** inflation and reduce the trade deficit.

e   but did much to **slow** it **down**.

f   from 17 per cent a month to less than 5 per cent.

1	2	3	4	5	6

C *Write the correct form of the appropriate phrasal verb in the space provided.*

1   Inflation is starting to _____.

2   He has made a series of proposals which he believes would help _____ land prices.

3   When she had _____ herself _____, she started the engine.

4   Harold _____ the car _____.

5   The text was too long so we _____ it _____.

6   We would like to stress that in no sense do we wish to _____ the importance of the issues raised.

Defeating and suppressing

back down   **knock down**   **pull down**   **put down**

Eventually he <u>backed down</u> on the question of seating.

I bumped into and nearly <u>knocked down</u> a person at the bus stop.

The council said it would close the flats and <u>pull</u> them <u>down</u>[1].

We've been encouraged all our life to <u>put down</u> women's talk.

[1] **Demolish** is a more formal word for **pull down**, and **knock down** means almost the same; **put up** means the opposite of **pull down**.

A   *Using your understanding of the examples above, write the correct phrasal verb to complete the definitions. Be careful with verb forms.*

1   If you _____ a building _____, you destroy it deliberately, so that the land it is on can be used.

2   If you _____ _____ on something, you accept someone else's point of view or agree to do what they want you to do, even though you do not really want to.

3   If you _____ _____ a person or their ideas, you criticize them and make them appear foolish or unimportant.

4   If you _____ someone _____, you hit them or push them deliberately or accidentally, so that they fall to the ground. If a car or other vehicle _____ someone _____, it hits them so that they fall to the ground and may be injured or killed.

B   *Match the phrases on the left with those on the right.*

1   She knew he wouldn't **back down**,   a   you almost **knocked** that woman **down**.
2   Don't drive so fast,   b   due to be **pulled down** next year.
3   A lot of people will be delighted   c   to see him **put down**.
4   Her flat is one of many   d   he had too much to lose.

1	2	3	4

C   *Write the correct form of the appropriate phrasal verb in the space provided.*

1   If someone _____ you _____ and is really mean and rotten to you, you should retaliate in some way.

2   Why did they _____ all those houses _____?

3   He threatened to prosecute us but he eventually _____.

4   I was nearly _____ by a hefty slap on the back.

Completing or failing

break down   **close down**   **let down**   **settle down**   **turn down**

An unhappy marriage which eventually <u>breaks down</u>[1] often results in disturbed children.
If the firms failed to make enough money, they would <u>close down</u>.
It would be best to run away now but she could not <u>let</u> Jimmie <u>down</u>: he needed help.
Alan told her that after this, he would <u>settle down</u> and marry her.
She applied for a job in a restaurant, but was <u>turned down</u>[2].

14

LANGUAGE COMMENT

¹ **Break down** also exists as a noun: *There was a serious <u>breakdown</u> of communication.*
² **Reject** means almost the same as **turn down**.

A   *Using your understanding of the examples above, write the correct phrasal verb to complete the definitions. Be careful with verb forms.*

1   When an arrangement, plan, or discussion _____ _____ , it fails because of a problem or disagreement.

2   If someone _____ _____ a factory or an organization, or if it _____ _____ , all work or activity stops there, usually for ever.

3   If you _____ _____ a person, their request, or their offer, you refuse their request or offer.

4   If you _____ _____ , you start living a quiet life in one place, often when you get married or buy a house.

5   If you _____ someone _____ , you fail to do something they have been relying on you to do.

B   *Match the phrases on the left with those on the right.*

1	I explained about his offer and said	a	the school system had **let** them
2	In the last 20 years that rural culture		**down**.
	has **broken down**	b	following a geological survey.
3	They felt strongly that	c	as people have flocked to the towns.
4	The mines had been **closed down**	d	and **settle down**.
5	You have to get a job	e	it was too good to **turn down**.

1	2	3	4	5

C   *Write the correct form of the appropriate phrasal verb in the space provided.*

1   You're so silly. You regularly _____ yourself _____ , don't you?

2   I have _____ an invitation for Saturday.

3   Garages are handy whenever the car _____ .

4   Paul will never _____ , he enjoys travelling too much.

5   The factory has had to be _____ due to the recession.

Writing and recording

DOWN

lay down   **put down to**   **take down**

There are laws which <u>lay down</u>[1] what employers and employees must and must not do.

All this can be <u>put down to</u> advances in engineering.

The postmistress began to <u>take down</u>[2] the message.

LANGUAGE COMMENT

[1] **Stipulate** is a more formal word for **lay down**.
[2] **Copy down, jot down, note down,** and **write down** all have similar meanings.

A *Using your understanding of the examples above, write the correct phrasal verb to complete the following definitions. Be careful with verb forms.*

1   If you _____ _____ what someone is saying, you listen to them and write it down or record it.

2   If you _____ one thing _____ _____ another thing, you believe that it is caused by another thing.

3   If laws, rules, or people in authority _____ _____ what people should do, they state that this is what must be done.

B *Match the phrases on the left with those on the right.*

1	He set up a tape recorder at Peter's bed	a to **take down** anything he might say.
2	The phenomenon is **put down**	b **to** the climate of violence in which the boy has grown up.
3	A government should **lay down**	c national policy for education.

1	2	3

C *Write the correct form of the appropriate phrasal verb in the space provided.*

1   Jill was _____ a story from Frank's dictation.

2   The policy has been _____ and agreed for years.

3   The whole thing will be _____ the unfortunate fact that the crisis occurred while the boss was away.

Consolidation

Write a paragraph on one of the following topics, including at least five of the phrasal verbs you have studied in this unit.

a   A problem for the government.

b   The marriage.

c   Finding a new job.

More verbs with 'down'

Use the space below to record other verbs with 'down' you find in your studies. Write down the meaning in the second column and keep a note of the sentence in which you find the verb in the third column. An example is given.

DOWN – DECREASING AND REDUCING		

DOWN – DEFEATING AND SUPPRESSING		

DOWN – COMPLETING OR FAILING		

DOWN – WRITING AND RECORDING		

DOWN – OTHER MEANINGS		
get down to	If you <u>get down to</u> something you start doing it seriously and with a lot of attention.	That's enough disruption for one day. I must <u>get down to</u> work.

Shown below are the two most important meanings of 'in' and one group of other meanings.

Under each of the headings you will see a list of the phrasal verbs which you are going to practise in the exercises given in this unit.

Inserting and absorbing	Being involved and active	Other meanings
put in	join in	fill in
sink in	put in	give in
take in	fit in	stay in

You can write other phrasal verbs with 'in' with related meanings in the space provided at the end of this unit. You can use a dictionary to help you.

Inserting and absorbing

put in   **sink in**   **take in**

If you pour hot water into a glass, <u>put</u> a spoon <u>in</u>[1] first to absorb the heat.

It took a moment or two for her words to <u>sink in</u>.

Mrs Stannard shook hands, her eyes <u>taking in</u> Karin from head to foot.

LANGUAGE COMMENT

[1] **Stick in** means almost the same as **put in**.

A   *Using your understanding of the examples above, write in the correct phrasal verb to complete the sentences. Be careful with verb forms.*

1   If you _____ _____ something that you see, read, or hear, you pay attention to it and are able to understand it, remember it, or evaluate it.

2   When a fact or idea, usually an unpleasant one, _____ _____, it gradually becomes recognized or understood.

3   If you _____ one thing _____ another, you place it inside the other thing.

B   *Match the phrases on the left with those on the right.*

1   He **puts in** the coins   a   listening and watching and **taking** it **in**.
2   The prisoners had nothing to do   b   and dials the number in Toulouse.
3   Alex had been the perfect pupil,   c   but let their situation **sink in**.

1	2	3

18

C *Write the correct form of the phrasal verb in the space provided.*

1   As he read out the documents and explained them, I _____ few of these details.

2   To design a car that goes faster the designer could either _____ a more powerful engine, or reduce the weight.

3   Has any of what I've been saying _____?

Being involved and active

join in   put in   fit in

When other games are played, he tries to join in.

Half of them were putting in forty-five hours a week or more.

You can't bring outsiders into a place like this; they wouldn't fit in; they would upset the whole atmosphere.

A *Using your understanding of the examples above, write in the correct phrasal verb to complete the sentences. Be careful with verb forms.*

1   If you _____ _____ as part of a group, you seem to belong there because you are similar to the other people in it.

2   If you _____ _____ an activity with other people, such as a meeting, you become involved in what they are doing.

3   If you _____ _____ time or effort doing something, you spend time or work hard doing it.

B *Match the phrases on the left with those on the right.*

1 Then they began to sing	a	to **fit in** with the locals.
2 I was certainly pleased by	b	and in a moment all the voices **joined in**.
3 They made every effort	c	the level of effort everyone **put in** today.

1	2	3

C *Write the correct form of the appropriate phrasal verb in the space provided.*

1   He had worked hard all his life, _____ overtime at the plant whenever he could get it.

2   Several people _____ the applause.

3   Each university has its own individual personality. Sometimes you can tell straight away if you are going to _____ or not.

Other meanings

fill in   **give in**   **stay in**

We _filled in_[1] all the customs forms.

The government said earlier that it would not _give in_[2] to pressure to change the law.

We _stayed in_[3] the whole evening, didn't go to the disco at all.

LANGUAGE COMMENT

[1] **Fill out** means almost the same as **fill in**.
[2] **Surrender** and **back down** mean almost the same as **give in**.
[3] **Stop in** means almost the same as **stay in**.

A   _Using your understanding of the examples above, write in the correct phrasal verb to complete the sentences. Be careful with verb forms._

1   If you _____ _____, you admit that you will have to do something you have been trying not to do, or that you will not be able to do something you wanted to do.

2   If you _____ _____, you remain at home rather than going out and enjoying yourself.

3   If you _____ _____ a form, you write all the information that is requested in the appropriate spaces.

B   _Match the phrases on the left with those on the right._

1 Ask for a claim form, **fill it in**	a	and send it to the social security office.
2 She was a domineering woman	b	I have to **stay in** and work.
3 I can't go out tonight,	c	and she didn't normally **give in** easily.

1	2	3

C   _Write the correct form of the appropriate phrasal verb in the space provided._

1   I don't like going out much, I prefer _____ with a good book.

2   _____ you name and address here.

3   She was certain only of one thing – she would not _____ to them.

Consolidation

Write a paragraph on one of the following topics, including at least three of the phrasal verbs you have studied in this unit.

a   The new girl.

b   Moving house.

c   A learning experience.

More verbs with 'in'

Use the space below to record other phrasal verbs with 'in' that you find in your studies. Write down the meaning in the second column and keep a note of the sentence in which you find the verb in the third column. An example is given.

IN – INSERTING AND ABSORBING		
plug in	If you plug something in, you connect it to an electricity supply by pushing its plug into an electrical socket.	I plugged in the kettle.

IN – BEING INVOLVED AND ACTIVE		

IN – OTHER MEANINGS		

21

Shown below are the three most important meanings of 'off' and one group of other meanings.

Under each of the headings you will see a list of the phrasal verbs which you are going to practise in the exercises given in this unit. Some verbs appear more than once, because many phrasal verbs have more than one meaning.

Leaving and beginning

drop off

see off

set off

take off

Rejecting and preventing

lay off

put off

write off

Stopping, cancelling, and finishing

call off

finish off

pay off

pull off

take off

Other meanings

go off (*two meanings*)

show off

tell off

wear off

You can write other phrasal verbs with 'off' with related meanings in the space provided at the end of this unit. You can use a dictionary to help you.

Leaving and beginning

drop off   see off   set off   take off

I can <u>drop</u> Daisy <u>off</u> on my way home.

She <u>saw</u> him <u>off</u> at the station.

He <u>set off</u>[1] on another of his European pleasure tours.

A steady stream of aircraft was <u>taking off</u> and landing.

LANGUAGE COMMENT

[1] **Set out, start out,** and **start off** mean almost the same as **set off**.

A   *Using your understanding of the examples above, write the correct phrasal verb to complete the definitions. Be careful with verb forms.*

1   When you _____ someone _____ , you go with them to the station, airport, or port that they are leaving from, and say goodbye to them there.

2   When you _____ _____ , you start a journey.

3   When you are driving, if you _____ one of your passengers _____ , you take them to where they want to go and leave them there.

4   When an aeroplane or bird _____ _____ , it leaves the ground and starts flying.

B *Match the phrases on the left with those on the right.*

1   If no one is **seeing** you **off,**   a   **taking off** on live television.
2   Could you **drop** me **off** at the post office? b   on my first trip to America by myself.
3   Chinese television showed the rocket   c   I'll take you.
4   I was about to **set off**   d   I have to send a parcel.

1	2	3	4

C *Write the correct form of the appropriate phrasal verb in the space provided.*

1   The plane came down in the Atlantic only one minute after _____.
2   Harry went with him to Zurich to _____ him _____.
3   Every morning I have to _____ the kids _____ at school.
4   We're _____ early on Sunday morning to avoid the traffic.

Rejecting and preventing

lay off   **put off**   **write off**

So if demand falls, the company <u>lays</u> men <u>off</u>[1].

Don't <u>put</u> it <u>off</u> till tomorrow.

'Whatever you do,' she pleaded, 'don't <u>write off</u> philosophy without even trying it.'

LANGUAGE COMMENT

[1] There is also a noun: *Textile companies announced 2,000 fresh <u>layoffs</u> last week.*

A *Using your understanding of the examples above, write the correct phrasal verb to complete the definitions. Be careful with verb forms.*

1   If you _____ someone or something _____, you decide that they are unimportant, useless, unlikely to be successful and that they are not worth further consideration.
2   If you_____ _____ an event or appointment, you delay or postpone it.
3   If workers are _____ _____, they are told by their employer that they have to leave their jobs because there is no more work for them to do.

B *Match the sentences and phrases on the left with those on the right.*

1   He can't be **put off** any more.   a   is not a solution to our financial problems.
2   **Laying off** workers   b   a failure after just a year.
3   You can't **write** him **off** as   c   You'll have to see him this week.

1	2	3

C *Write the correct form of the appropriate phrasal verb in the space provided.*

1   They kept _____ signing the paper.
2   City workers are being _____ at the rate of 100 a week.
3   Michael's still the world record-holder, so you can never _____ him _____.

Stopping, cancelling, and finishing

call off   finish off   pay off   pull off   take off

On the eve of her departure the strike was definitely <u>called off</u>, and she was sure of her flight.
We had to work until midnight to <u>finish</u> them <u>off</u>[1].
He had used the firm's money to <u>pay off</u>[2] gambling debts.
If I could <u>pull</u> it <u>off</u>[3] it'd be my first win over Alex.
Bill and I <u>took</u> time <u>off</u> from work and flew to France.

LANGUAGE COMMENT

[1] **Polish off** is an informal expression for **finish off**.
[2] **Repay** means almost the same as **pay off**.
[3] **Bring off** and **carry off** mean almost the same as **pull off**.

A *Using your understanding of the examples above, write the correct phrasal verb to complete the definitions. Be careful with verb forms.*

1 If you _____ something _____, you succeed in doing something which is very difficult to achieve.

2 If you _____ time _____, you spend it doing something different from your normal routine or job.

3 If you _____ _____ something that you are doing, you complete it by doing the last part.

4 If you _____ _____ an event or an arrangement that has been planned, you cancel it.

5. If you _____ _____ a debt or bill, you give someone the total amount of money that you owe them so that you are no longer in debt.

B *Match the phrases on the left with those on the right.*

1 If you can't behave yourself,
2 Until further notice I have been **taken off**
3 The most common reason for borrowing
4 He was **finishing off** his lunch
5 She had succeeded, triumphantly:

a we might as well **call** the whole thing **off**.
b she had **pulled** it **off**.
c when I arrived at his home in Malibu.
d is to **pay off** existing loans.
e all routine duties and given a rather special job.

1	2	3	4	5

C *Write the correct form of the appropriate phrasal verb in the space provided.*

1 They hoped that the strike would be _____.
2 We decided to go back and _____ the wine.
3 You have to _____ Christmas Day as a holiday.
4 It's never been done before; yet they may well _____ it _____.
5 So she fell into debt and had to _____ it _____ by selling her house.

24

Other meanings

go off   show off   tell off   wear off

The gun <u>went off</u> as he was putting it away.

Food that has <u>gone off</u>[1] has been infected with bacteria that cause illness.

He was afraid the others might think he was <u>showing off</u>[2] or being superior.

When I was <u>told off</u>[3] by my parents, it was nearly always justified.

The effect of the aspirin had <u>worn off</u> and her toothache had come back.

LANGUAGE COMMENT

[1] **Decay** is a more formal word for **go off**.
[2] This meaning of **show off** is used to show disapproval.
[3] **Reprimand** is a formal word for **tell off**.

A   *Using your understanding of the examples above, write the correct phrasal verb to complete the definitions. Be careful with verb forms.*

1   When a feeling _____ _____, it disappears slowly until it no longer exists or has any effect.

2   If you _____ _____, you try to impress people by making your skills or good qualities very obvious.

3   If food or drink _____ _____, it becomes stale, sour, or rotten.

4   If you _____ someone _____, you speak to them angrily because they have done something wrong.

5   If a gun _____ _____, it is fired. If a bomb _____ _____, it explodes.

B   *Match the phrases on the left with those on the right.*

1   Stop **showing off**.   a   **going off** by accident is slight.
2   By the next afternoon   b   Everybody's bored with your stories.
3   Smell this, will you?   c   the shock had **worn off**.
4   Don't **tell** me **off** again, Dad,   d   I think it's **gone off**.
5   The probability of a nuclear weapon   e   I did my best.

1	2	3	4	5

C   *Write the correct form of the appropriate phrasal verb in the space provided.*

1   The milk's _____ again.

2   These feelings _____ once the user has stopped taking the drug.

3   My mother _____ me _____ for not clearing up my room.

4   I could hear the bombs _____.

5   There were lots of kids _____ on the diving board.

Consolidation

Write a paragraph on one of the following topics, including a least five of the phrasal verbs you have studied in this unit.

a   The holiday.

b   A debt.

c   Saying goodbye.

More verbs with 'off'

Use the space below to record other phrasal verbs with 'off' you find in your studies. Write down the meaning in the second column and keep a note of the sentence in which you find the verb in the third column. An example is given.

OFF – LEAVING AND BEGINNING		

OFF – REJECTING AND PREVENTING		

OFF – STOPPING, CANCELLING, AND FINISHING		
break off	If you <u>break off</u> a relationship or agreement, you end it.	The government has warned that it may <u>break off</u> peace talks with the country's left-wing guerillas.

OFF – OTHER MEANINGS		

Shown below is the most important meaning of 'on' and one group of other meanings.

Under each of the headings you will see a list of the phrasal verbs which you are going to practise in the exercises given in this unit. Some verbs appear more than once, because many phrasal verbs have more than one meaning.

Continuing and progressing | ## Other meanings

come on

get on (*two meanings*)

go on

pass on

stay on

get on

go on (*two meanings*)

take on

move on to

You can write other phrasal verbs with 'on' with related meanings in the space provided at the end of the unit. You can use a dictionary to help you.

Continuing and progressing

come on   get on   go on   pass on   stay on

How's your house coming on [1]? When will it be finished?

Oh, yes, Mary is getting on [2] well. First in her class last week.

Perhaps we can get on with the meeting.

They simply can't go on [3] saying everything is fine, when it clearly isn't.

The union head office may be able to pass on [4] helpful information.

Pupils have to stay on [5] at school till they are 16.

LANGUAGE COMMENT

[1] **Come along** means almost the same as **come on**.
[2] **Get along** means almost the same as **get on**.
[3] **Carry on** and **keep on** mean almost the same as **go on**.
[4] **Send on** is similar to **pass on** except that it implies sending something by post.
[5] **Leave** means the opposite of **stay on**.

A   *Using your understanding of the examples above, write the correct phrasal verb to complete the definitions. Be careful with verb forms.*

1   If you _____ _____ doing something, you continue to do it.

2   If you ask how someone is _____ _____ with an activity, you are asking about their progress.

3   If you _____ _____ with an activity, you start doing or continue doing it.

4   If something is _____ _____, it is making progress or developing.

5   If you _____ _____ somewhere, you remain there longer than other people, longer than in the past on longer than you planned.

6   If you _____ something _____ to someone, you give it to them, for example after you have used it or after someone else has given it to you.

27

B *Match the phrases on the left with those on the right.*

1 I couldn't **go on**
2 I must know your name
3 I am very happy and
4 However, I'm seriously thinking
   of letting her **stay on**.
5 My new book is
6 How's your son **getting on** at school?

a She seems to be a very nice girl.
b if I am to **pass on** the information.
c looking forward to **getting on** with
   the job.
d living with him.
e He seems to be doing very well.
f **coming on** quite well now.

1	2	3	4	5	6

C *Write the correct form of the appropriate phrasal verb in the space provided.*

1 You would be approached and asked if you would like to _____
   as a permanent member of the staff.

2 Most men do not do these things: they're too busy _____ with
   their work.

3 Philip assured her that he had _____ the invitation.

4 You should have been _____ with your translation in the
   meantime.

5 Then she dismissed guilt as self-indulgence and _____ with the
   business of loving him.

6 He must've _____ a bit in eight hours!

Other meanings

get on   **go on**   **move on to**   **take on**

He feels he may have been responsible. He has never <u>got on</u>[1] well with his son.

'My dear Pluskat,' he said icily, 'we don't know yet what's <u>going on</u>[2]. We'll let you know when we find out.'

There is no reason why an English graduate can't <u>go on</u>[3] to train as an accountant.

Next we <u>move on to</u>[4] news from the world of business and finance.

Now when we <u>take on</u> a job, we run it ourselves and that way we have complete control.

LANGUAGE COMMENT

[1] **Get along** means almost the same as **get on**.
[2] **Happen** means almost the same as **go on**.
[3] **Move on**, **press on**, and **push on** all have similar meanings. **Go on** is usually followed by the infinitive 'to do' or the preposition 'to'.
[4] **Come on to**, **get on to**, **go on to**, **pass on to**, and **turn to** mean almost the same as **move on to**.

A *Using your understanding of the examples above, write the correct phrasal verb to complete the definitions. Be careful with verb forms.*

1 If you say that something is _____ _____, you mean that it is taking place at the present time.

2 If you _____ _____ to do something, you do it after you have finished something else.

3 If you _____ _____ a new job, task, or responsibility, you accept it and try to do what is required.

4 If you _____ _____ with someone, you like them and have a friendly relationship with them.

5 If you _____ _____ _____ a particular topic, you bring that topic into a conversation or lecture after you have been talking about something else.

B *Match the phrases on the left with those on the right.*

1	Now he's made the breakthrough,	a	the second part of our conversation.
2	One of the most astute of Hollywood agents	b	and that she would be good with Max.
		c	to figure out what was **going on**.
3	Perhaps we may now **move on to**	d	had **taken on** the job of trying to
4	I felt I could really **get on** with her		sell Mr Nixon's memoirs.
5	I spent three weeks down there trying	e	I'm sure he'll **go on** to achieve more.

1	2	3	4	5

C *Write the correct form of the appropriate phrasal verb in the space provided.*

1 'Let's _____ to compare teacher/student ratios and costs in higher education.'

2 Can we _____ the next point on the agenda?

3 She _____ more work than is good for her.

4 The first problem was to find out what was actually _____.

5 It could have been difficult because, as you know, if I don't _____ someone, I can't hide it.

Consolidation

Write a paragraph on one of the following topics, including at least three of the phrasal verbs you have studied in this unit.

a The last day at school.

b The meeting.

c Making progress.

More verbs with 'on'

Use the space below to record other phrasal verbs with 'on' you find in your studies. Write down the meaning in the second column and keep a note of the sentence in which you find the verb in the third column. An example is given.

ON – CONTINUING AND PROGRESSING		
drag on	If an event or process <u>drags on</u>, it progresses very slowly and takes longer than seems necessary.	The expectation in parliament is clearly that the crisis will <u>drag on</u> for some time.

ON – OTHER MEANINGS		

Shown below are the four most important meanings of 'out' and one group of other meanings.

Under each of the headings you will see a list of the phrasal verbs which you are going to practise in the exercises given in this unit.

Leaving and beginning

break out

go out

set out

take out

Removing and excluding

cross out

get out of

keep out

knock out

leave out

talk out of

throw out

Searching and finding

check out

find out

make out

try out

turn out

Ending or disappearing

run out

sell out

wear out

wipe out

Other meanings

carry out

fall out

give out

look out

sort out

You can write other phrasal verbs with 'out' with related meanings in the space provided at the end of this unit. You can use a dictionary to help you.

Leaving and beginning

break out   go out   set out   take out

When war <u>broke out</u> [1] my father joined the Navy and he was drowned at sea.

I have to <u>go out</u>, I'll be back late tonight.

I didn't <u>set out</u> [2] to be successful, but I knew that I didn't want to do something dull and boring for a living.

Why don't you <u>take</u> the children <u>out</u>?

LANGUAGE COMMENT

[1] There is also a noun: *a severe <u>outbreak</u> of food poisoning.*

[2] **Set off, start off,** and **start out** mean almost the same as **set out**.
There is also a noun: *You should explain this to him at the <u>outset</u>.*

A *Using your understanding of the examples above, write the correct phrasal verb to complete the definitions. Be careful with verb forms.*

1   If you _____ someone _____, for example to a restaurant or a film, they go there with you, and you pay for everything.

2   When you _____ _____, you start a journey. If you _____ _____ to do something, you start taking action or making plans with the intention of achieving a particular result.

3   If something unpleasant _____ _____, it begins suddenly.

4   When you _____ _____, you leave your house and go somewhere else, for example in order to shop, visit friends, or see a film.

B *Match the phrases on the left with those on the right.*

1	After breakfast	a	because she had **gone out** shopping.
2	He offered to **take** us **out**	b	Do you have regular fire drill practice?
3	He could not ask her immediately	c	for a drink or something.
4	Would you know what to do if a fire **broke out** in your work place?	d	you **set out** on safari.

1	2	3	4

C *Write the correct form of the appropriate phrasal verb in the space provided.*

1   Rioting has _____ at Strangeways Prison in Manchester, in the north of England.

2   We'd talk for hours, _____ for days in the country, even spend weekends away.

3   I _____ Andrea _____ to dinner one evening.

4   I got my letters and papers together and _____ for the address he gave me. It wasn't far.

Removing and excluding

cross out   get out of   keep out   knock out   leave out   talk out of throw out

You haven't got time to rewrite it, just <u>cross out</u>[1] clearly what you want to change and write it above.

I think they're trying to <u>get out of</u>[2] their obligations under the agreement.

They had a guard dog to <u>keep out</u> intruders.

The tablet had <u>knocked</u> her <u>out</u> for four hours.

One or two scenes in the play were <u>left out</u>[3] of the performance.

He tried to <u>talk</u> me <u>out of</u>[4] buying such a big car.

I can't remember my parents <u>throwing out</u>[5] their old furniture.

32

LANGUAGE COMMENT

[1] **Delete** means almost the same as **cross out**.
[2] This is an informal use. **Wriggle out of** means almost the same as **get out of**.
[3] **Miss out** means almost the same as **leave out**.
[4] **Talk into** means the opposite of **talk out of**.
[5] **Throw away** means almost the same as **throw out**.

A *Using your understanding of the examples above, write the correct phrasal verb to complete the definitions. Be careful with verb forms.*

1 To _____ someone or something _____ of a place means to prevent them from entering it or being there.

2 If you _____ _____ _____ doing something, you avoid doing it.

3 If you _____ someone _____ _____ doing something, you persuade them not to do it.

4 If you _____ _____ one or more words on a page, you draw a line through them, usually because they are wrong or because you do not want people to read them.

5 To _____ someone _____ means to cause them to become unconscious or to fall asleep, or to eliminate them, for example from a competition.

6 If you _____ someone or something _____, you do not include them in an activity or group.

7 If you _____ _____ an object you no longer want, you get rid of it, for example by putting it in the dustbin. If you _____ _____ someone's ideas or suggestions, you reject them because you find them unacceptable.

B *Match the phrases on the left with those on the right.*

1 We only had two blankets   a simply **cross** it **out** and continue.
2 The explosion hurt no one   b so you will have to **leave** me **out**.
3 Why on earth are you going, then?   c I've made up my mind.
4 If you make a mistake   d when they found she was pregnant.
5 It's no use trying to **talk** me **out of** it, e It's too late to **get out of** it.
6 Her parents **threw** her **out**   f to **keep out** the cold.
7 I shan't be available   g except it **knocked out** the colonel.

1	2	3	4	5	6	7

C *Write the correct form of the appropriate phrasal verb in the space provided.*

1 Just go through it and check you haven't _____ anything _____.

2 I couldn't _____ writing the script, I was contractually committed.

3 Now and then he frowned, _____ something _____ and rewrote it.

33

4   The fall off her horse had been hard enough to _____ her _____.

5   Mama would not let us _____ the box of old photographs we found under the sofa.

6   She stamped her feet on the pavement to _____ the cold.

7   I spent the whole of last night trying to _____ her _____ resigning.

Searching and finding

check out   find out   make out   try out   turn out

It might be difficult to transfer your money, so <u>check</u> it <u>out</u> with the manager.

I'm only interested in <u>finding out</u>[1] what the facts are.

It is sometimes difficult to <u>make out</u> what is said over an airport loudspeaker.

The tastes vary, so it's worth <u>trying out</u> different brands.

Nothing, he had learned, ever <u>turned out</u> the way one imagined.

LANGUAGE COMMENT

[1] **Discover** means almost the same as **find out**.

A   *Using your understanding of the examples above, write the correct phrasal verb to complete the definitions. Be careful with verb forms.*

1   If something or someone _____ _____ to be a particular thing, they are discovered to be that thing.

2   If you _____ something _____, you manage to see or hear it.

3   If you _____ something _____, you find out about it or examine it because you want to make sure that everything is correct or safe.

4   If you _____ something _____, you test it in order to discover how useful or effective it is.

5   If you _____ _____ something, you learn something that you did not already know.

B   *Match the phrases on the left with those on the right.*

1 In the darkness	a	was the ideal man for the job.
2 Frank was going to **check out** the restaurant	b	before we buy it.
	c	to see whether anything unusual was going on.
3 Let's **try it out**		
4 We **found out**	d	that she was wrong.
5 It **turned out** that Richard	e	it was hard to **make out** his features.

1	2	3	4	5

C   Write the correct form of the appropriate phrasal verb in the space provided.

1   A police officer _____ the statement Mrs Mossman had just made.

2   The Marvin's house _____ to be an old converted barn.

3   It's best to _____ this _____ first on a bit of spare fabric.

4   Can you _____ how much it costs?

5   He could just _____ the number plate of the car.

Ending or disappearing

run out   sell out   wear out   wipe out

We were rapidly _running out_ of money.

Shops almost immediately _sold out_ of the advertised goods.

Visitors _wear us out_[1] more than the children do.

Epidemics _wiped out_[2] the local population.

LANGUAGE COMMENT

[1] **Exhaust** and **tire out** mean almost the same as **wear out**.

[2] **Eradicate** is a more formal word for **wipe out**.

A   Using your understanding of the examples above, write the correct phrasal verb to complete the definitions. Be careful with verb forms.

1   If a shop is or has _____ _____ of something, it has all been sold, and there is none of it left in the shop.

2   If you _____ _____ of something, or if something _____ _____, you have no more of it left.

3   If something _____ you _____, it makes you become so tired that you cannot continue what you were doing.

4   To _____ someone or something _____ means to destroy or get rid of them completely.

B   Match the phrases on the left with those on the right.

1 Can I use your lighter?	a	the memory of his years in prison.
2 That isn't show jumping.	b	I've **run out** of matches.
3 Could I buy some sun cream?	c	Sorry, we've **sold out**.
4 He was determined to **wipe out**	d	It's a marathon designed to **wear** the horse **out**.

1	2	3	4

C   Write the correct form of the appropriate phrasal verb in the space provided.

1   We must _____ starvation and preventable disease.

2   I'm sorry we've _____ of that particular brand.

3   It looks as if oil will _____ faster than coal.

4   They _____ us _____ with their constant screaming and crying.

35

Other meanings

carry out   fall out   give out   look out   sort out

The first experiments were <u>carried out</u> by Dr Preston McLendon.

She had <u>fallen out</u> so severely with her parents that she couldn't go home.

They also <u>give out</u> information about courses for teachers of English.

'<u>Look out</u>,' I said. 'There's someone coming.'

It was an intelligence test, intended to <u>sort out</u> the children capable of attempting the papers.

A   *Using your understanding of the examples above, write the correct phrasal verb to complete the definitions. Be careful with verb forms.*

1   You say or shout _____ _____ to warn someone that they are in danger.

2   If you _____ _____ a number of things, you distribute them among a number of different people.

3   If you _____ _____ with someone, you have an argument and are no longer friendly with them.

4   If you _____ _____ a group of things, you consider them carefully and divide them into categories that are clearly different from each other.

5   If you _____ _____ a task, you do it.

B   *Match the phrases on the left with those on the right.*

1   Some employers **give out** a lot of   a   I'm going to drop a rock,' I shouted.
     information;   b   has just **carried out** a survey.

2   '**Look out**,   c   others refuse to part with any.

3   'Woman' magazine   d   to **sort out** fact from fiction.

4   Their mothers **fell out** at the wedding e   and they haven't spoken since.

5   It is difficult

1	2	3	4	5

C   *Write the correct form of the appropriate phrasal verb in the space provided.*

1   It was the only time we ever _____, in all those years together.

2   Howard _____ drinks to his guests.

3   Such a policy will only be _____ if his Party achieves office.

4   The remaining girls were collecting and _____ the balls.

5   '_____!' shouted Joe. 'He has a gun!'

Consolidation

Write a paragraph on one of the following topics, using at least five of the phrasal verbs you have studied in this unit.

a   A police investigation.

b   A sea voyage.

c   Public opinion.

More verbs with 'out'

Use the space below to record other verbs with 'out' you find in your studies. Write down the meaning in the second column and keep a note of the sentence in which you find the verb in the third column. An example is given.

OUT – LEAVING AND BEGINNING		

OUT – REMOVING AND EXCLUDING		
rule out	If you rule out an idea or a course of action, you decide that it is impossible or unsuitable.	They can't rule out the possibility that he was kidnapped.

OUT – SEARCHING AND FINDING		

OUT – ENDING OR DISAPPEARING		

OUT – OTHER MEANINGS		

Shown below are the two most important meanings of 'over' and one group of other meanings.

Under each of the headings you will see a list of the phrasal verbs which you are going to practise in the exercises given in this unit. Some verbs appear more than once, because many phrasal verbs have more than one meaning.

Considering and communicating	**Changing and transferring**	**Other meanings**
put over	take over (*two meanings*)	get over
talk over	win over	get over with
think over	run over	

You can write other phrasal verbs with 'over' with related meanings in the space provided at the end of this unit. You can use a dictionary to help you.

Considering and communicating

put over   **talk over**   **think over**

What they talk about is less important than the way they <u>put</u> it <u>over</u>[1].

I'll <u>talk</u> it <u>over</u> with Len tonight and let you know tomorrow.

He said he would leave me alone to <u>think</u> things <u>over</u>[2] for five minutes.

LANGUAGE COMMENT

[1] **Put across, get across,** and **get over** all have similar meanings.
[2] **Chew over, mull over,** and **turn over** mean almost the same as **think over,** and **consider** is a slightly more formal word.

A   *Using your understanding of the examples above, write the correct phrasal verb to complete the definitions. Be careful with verb forms.*

1   When you _____ an idea _____, you succeed in describing or explaining it to someone.

2   If you _____ something _____, you discuss it with someone.

3   If you _____ something _____, you consider it carefully before making a decision.

B   *Match the phrases on the left with those on the right.*

1 I can see you have doubts;	a	take the day to **think** it **over.**
2 There's plenty of opportunity for you	b	you can **put** a message **over** nationally or world-wide.
3 With the modern resources available,		
	c	to **talk** it **over** with someone.

1	2	3

C   *Write the correct form of the appropriate phrasal verb in the space provided.*

1   How to _____ it _____ to the class, that's the trouble.

2   We all met in Pat's room, to _____ what we had seen.

3   Dale hadn't refused but he had wanted more time to _____ it _____.

Changing and transferring

take over   **win over**

Some people wanted to <u>take over</u>[1] my father's oil importing business.

He was 'Jacko' Reed, a former rugby star who had recently <u>taken over</u> as manager of the bank's main branch in the city.

Local radio stations have done their best to <u>win over</u>[2] new audiences.

> **LANGUAGE COMMENT**
>
> [1] There is also a noun: *The trend towards <u>takeovers</u> has intensified.*
> [2] **Win round** means almost the same as **win over**.

A   *Using your understanding of the examples above, write the correct phrasal verb to complete the definitions. Be careful with verb forms.*

1   If you _____ _____ a job or a responsibility, you start doing it or being responsible for it after someone else has finished.

2   If you _____ someone _____, you persuade them to support you or agree with you.

3   To _____ _____ a company or a country means to gain control of it.

B   *Match the phrases on the left with those on the right.*

1   Well-trained and equipped troops   a   could probably **take over** the country.
2   A new chairman or managing   b   isn't too familiar with the procedures.
    director who has just **taken over**   c   by the courtesy and direct simplicity
3   I was completely **won over**   of the people.

1	2	3

C   *Write the correct form of the appropriate phrasal verb in the space provided.*

1   The I.P.C. was _____ by the huge Reed Paper Group.

2   Benn had succeeded in _____ those in authority to the workers' cause.

3   One report says another group of soldiers _____ the main airport.

39

Other meanings

get over   get over with   run over

It took me a very long time to <u>get over</u> the shock of her death.

Let's try and <u>get</u> this meeting <u>over with</u> as quickly as possible.

The sweat rolled down my neck, and we almost <u>ran over</u>[1] some little animal or other that was crossing the road.

LANGUAGE COMMENT

[1] **Run down, knock down,** and **knock over** mean almost the same as **run over**.

A Using your understanding of the examples above, write the correct phrasal verb to complete the definitions. Be careful with verb forms.

1 If a vehicle _____ _____ someone or something, it hits them or drives over them causing injury or damage.

2 If you _____ something _____ _____, you do and complete something unpleasant that must be done.

3 If you _____ _____ an illness or other unpleasant experience, you recover from it.

B Match the phrases on the left with those on the right.

1 What would happen if I were to	a	to **get over** his cold.
2 He is taking a long time	b	as quickly as possible.
3 He wanted to **get** it **over with**	c	get **run over** by a bus?

1	2	3

C Write the correct form of the appropriate phrasal verb in the space provided.

1 Give Woods his final warning now and _____ it _____.

2 He was completely out of control and narrowly avoided _____ a group of pedestrians.

3 It has helped me to _____ the emotional crisis and tragedy.

Consolidation

Write a paragraph on one of the following topics, using at least four of the phrasal verbs you have studied in this unit.

a   The election.

b   The accident.

c   The managing director.

More verbs with 'over'

OVER

Use the space below to record other verbs with 'over' you find in your studies. Write down the meaning in the second column and keep a note of the sentence in which you find the verb in the third column. An example is given.

OVER – CONSIDERING AND COMMUNICATING		

OVER – CHANGING AND TRANSFERRING		
change over	To change over from one thing to another means to stop doing one thing and change to something else.	He also changed over to a new manner of presentation.

OVER – OTHER MEANINGS		

Shown below are the six most important meanings of 'up' and one group of other meanings.

Under each of the headings you will see a list of the phrasal verbs which you are going to practise in the exercises given in this unit. Some verbs appear more than once, because many phrasal verbs have more than one meaning.

Increasing and improving

bring up	go up
brush up	grow up
build up	save up
cheer up	

Preparing

dress up
fix up
set up
warm up

Approaching

catch up
face up to
keep up
live up to

Disrupting and damaging

blow up
break up
hold up
mess up
mix up

Completing and finishing

check up	give up
cover up	sum up
do up	tidy up
end up	use up

Happening and creating

bring up
come up
come up with
make up
think up

Other meanings

look up	put up with
make up	take up
make up for	turn up
pick up	

You can write other phrasal verbs with 'up' with related meanings in the space provided at the end of this unit. You can use a dictionary to help you.

Increasing and improving

bring up   **brush up**   **build up**   **cheer up**   **go up**   **grow up**   **save up**

I brought up two children alone.
I need to brush up my English: I haven't used it for seven years.
We helped to build up the wealth of this country.
Her friends tried to cheer her up, telling her she wasn't missing much.
The price of petrol and oil related products will go up[1].
We had similar backgrounds; we both grew up in small villages.
They're saving up money for a holiday.

LANGUAGE COMMENT

1 **Rise** means almost the same as **go up.**

A *Using your understanding of the examples above, write the correct phrasal verb to complete the definitions. Be careful with verb forms.*

1 If something _____ _____ or if you _____ it _____, it gradually increases in amount, size, or intensity.

2 When you _____ _____ or when something or someone _____ you _____, you stop feeling depressed and become happier.

3 If you _____ _____, or _____ _____ money, you collect money by not spending it, usually so that you can buy something you want.

4 When you _____ _____ a child, you look after it until it is grown up, and you try to give it particular beliefs and attitudes.

5 As you _____ _____, you gradually change from being a child to being an adult.

6 If the cost, level, standard, or amount of something _____ _____, it becomes more expensive, higher, or greater than it was before.

7 If you _____ _____ a subject you know but have not used for a while, you improve your knowledge of it.

B *Match the sentences and phrases on the left with those on the right.*

1	Unemployment is expected	a	when you **grow up**?
2	If too much pressure **builds up,**	b	to **brush up** his German.
3	It gave him a chance	c	to **cheer** herself **up.**
4	She bought strawberries	d	to **go up** over the coming months.
5	What do you want to be	e	to put a child through school.
6	Fathers are playing a bigger role	f	it will explode.
7	The relatives will **save up**	g	in **bringing up** children.

1	2	3	4	5	6	7

C *Write the correct form of the appropriate phrasal verb in the space provided.*

1 It'll take me at least a year to _____ for a new guitar.

2 The Prime Minister believes children are best _____ in a stable relationship, by a loving mother and father.

3 When you go shopping all you hear is how everything has _____.

4 If you are unemployed and haven't had an interview for a long time, it's a good idea to _____ on your interview technique.

5 I've lived in London for seven years, but I was _____ in Newcastle.

6 We're trying to _____ a collection of herbs and spices.

7 _____! It's not the end of the world, you know.

43

Preparing

dress up   fix up   set up   warm up

Rather than sit at home, they all get <u>dressed up</u> and go out.

Have you done anything about <u>fixing up</u>[1] a meeting place?

The first thing to do in a crisis is to <u>set up</u> a committee.

Shall we have a game straight away, or would you rather <u>warm up</u>[2] first?

LANGUAGE COMMENT

[1] **Arrange** is a more formal word for **fix up**, and **line up** means almost the same.

[2] **Limber up** and **loosen up** mean almost the same as **warm up**.
There is also a noun and an adjective: *During the <u>warm-up</u> exercises, I was still shaking.*

A   *Using your understanding of the examples above, write the correct phrasal verb to complete the definitions. Be careful with verb forms.*

1   If you _____ something _____, you make the arrangements that are necessary to achieve it.

2   If you _____ _____ just before a physical event or activity such as a race, you prepare yourself for it, usually by practising or doing some exercises.

3   If you _____ _____, you put on clothes that are smarter than the ones you usually wear because you are going somewhere special.

4   If you _____ something _____, you make the arrangements and preparations that are necessary for it to start.

B   *Match the phrases on the left with those on the right.*

1   I can't be bothered   a   to **fix up** a taxi for you.
2   You can ask Jane   b   to **dress up** this evening.
3   She is **warming up** on another court, c   selling toy guns by mail order.
4   He has now **set up** a company   d   preparing for the match.

1	2	3	4

C   *Write the correct form of the appropriate phrasal verb in the space provided.*

1   They had been trained in a special school _____ by Brigadier James Gavin.

2   I _____ an appointment to see her and she showed me what she did and chatted to me.

3   I never get _____ when I'm invited somewhere, I always go as I am.

4   They jogged around the track twice to _____.

Approaching

catch up   face up to   keep up   live up to

She stood still, allowing him to <u>catch</u> her <u>up</u>.

They all conclude that global warming is a real problem the world will have to <u>face up to</u> sooner or later.

Penny tended to work through her lunch hour in an effort to <u>keep up</u> with her work.

The film didn't <u>live up to</u>[1] my expectations.

LANGUAGE COMMENT

[1] **Measure up to** and **match up to** mean almost the same as **live up to**.

A   *Using your understanding of the examples above, write the correct phrasal verb to complete the definitions. Be careful with verb forms.*

1   If you _____ _____ _____ a difficult situation, you accept it and deal with it.

2   If someone or something _____ _____ _____ people's expectations, they are as good as they are expected to be.

3   If you _____ _____, you work at the necessary speed so that you do as well as other people or get all your work done in the required time.

4   If you _____ _____ with someone, you reach the same standard, level, or place as they are.

B   *Match the phrases on the left with those on the right.*

1 His marks are fine	a you're going to have to work very hard to **catch up**.
2 His situation was desperate,	
3 If you're absent for two weeks,	b but he **faced up to** it.
4 The only question is this:	c can he **live up to** their expectations?
	d and he has no trouble **keeping up**.

1	2	3	4

C   *Write the correct form of the appropriate phrasal verb in the space provided.*

1   'Hey, wait up,' he called out, _____ with them at the foot of the stairs.

2   She succeeded, to my mind, in _____ her extraordinary reputation.

3   They've got to _____ some very tough economic problems, haven't they?

4   Credit card companies were struggling to _____ with the pace of spending.

Disrupting and damaging

blow up   break up   hold up   mess up   mix up

They now have enough nuclear weapons to <u>blow</u> themselves <u>up</u> many times over.
The Soviet Union has <u>broken up</u>.
Arguments over budget deficits have <u>held up</u>[1] the negotiations.
If she got caught with me now it would <u>mess up</u>[2] the rest of her life.
I have somehow <u>mixed up</u> two events.

LANGUAGE COMMENT

[1] **Delay** means almost the same as **hold up**.
[2] This is an informal use. **Screw up** means almost the same as **mess up**, but is very informal.

A   *Using your understanding of the examples above, write the correct phrasal verb to complete the following definitions. Be careful with verb forms.*

1   If you _____ something _____ or if it _____ _____, it is destroyed by an explosion.

2   If someone or something _____ _____ an activity or arrangement, they delay it or make it late.

3   If you _____ _____ something that has been carefully made or done, you spoil it.

4   When something _____ _____ or when you _____ it _____, it becomes divided into smaller parts.

5   If you _____ _____ two things or people, you confuse them, so that you think that one of them is the other one.

B   *Match the phrases on the left with those on the right.*

1 This is an update,	a	She's really **messed** it **up** this time.
2 Well, gentlemen, any other business?	b	He might be a minute or two late.
3 How can anyone do such a bad job?	c	and sank.
4 He said he'd been **held up**.	d	don't **mix** it **up** with the other version.
5 One of the submarines **blew up**	e	If not, we'll **break up** the meeting now.

1	2	3	4	5

C   *Write the correct form of the appropriate phrasal verb in the space provided.*

1   If there's any delay, it'll _____ the rest of our plans.

2   The battleship Maine has been _____ in Havana Harbour.

3   Their marriage is _____.

4   People even _____ us _____ and greet us by each other's names.

5   The amount of animal research being carried out is probably _____ progress rather than increasing it.

Completing and finishing

check up   cover up   do up   end up   give up   sum up   tidy up   use up

The council had <u>checked up</u> on her and decided that she was unsuitable for employment.

He alleged that the President knew about Watergate and tried to <u>cover</u> it <u>up</u>[1].

I can't <u>do</u> my top button <u>up</u>[2].

If we go on in this way, we shall <u>end up</u>[3] with millions and millions of unemployed.

I'll never be able to <u>give up</u> smoking.

I can't <u>sum up</u> his whole philosophy in one sentence.

He went back to the studio and <u>tidied</u> it <u>up</u>[4].

He <u>used up</u> all the coins he had.

LANGUAGE COMMENT

[1] **Conceal** and **suppress** are more formal words for **cover up**.
There is also a noun: *He denied that he took any part in the <u>cover-up</u>.*
[2] **Fasten up** means almost the same as **do up**. **Belt up**, **button up**, **tie up**, and **zip up** are all similar but are more specific.
[3] **Finish up** and **wind up** mean almost the same as **end up**.
[4] **Clear up** means almost the same as **tidy up**.

A   *Using your understanding of the examples above, write the correct phrasal verb to complete the definitions. Be careful with verb forms.*

1   If you _____ something _____, you fasten it.

2   If you _____ _____ in a particular place or situation, you are in that place or situation after a series of events, even though you did not originally intend to be.

3   If you _____ _____ a supply of something, you finish it so that none of it is left.

4   If you _____ _____ an activity or belief, you stop doing it or believing in it.

5   If you _____ _____ a situation, you state briefly its most important aspects or characteristics.

6   If you _____ _____ on someone or something, you obtain information about them, often secretly.

7   When you _____ _____ a place, a container, or the things in them, you put all the things back in their proper places so that the place or container is neat again.

8   If you _____ _____ something that you do not want people to know about, you hide it from them.

B   *Match the sentences and phrases on the left with those on the right.*

1	They think there is a security leak	a	and put it away in my locker.
2	Aren't there any more cassettes?	b	pulling fiercely at the laces.
3	She has **given up** her job in computing	c	no house and a two-year-old child.
4	Sylvia **ended up** with no money,	d	if the public find out, we're finished.
5	But you could **sum up** what they said	e	to pursue her passion for catering.
6	He started to **do up** his boots,	f	No, we've **used** them all **up**.

47

7 **Tidy** everything **up**
8 It has to be **covered up**:

g   and are trying to **check up**.
h   in two or three words.

1	2	3	4	5	6	7	8

C *Write the correct form of the appropriate phrasal verb in the space provided.*

1 She never completely _____ hope.
2 Two of my friends _____ in prison for armed robbery.
3 Silently I pulled the door closed and _____ my boots.
4 If we go on spending like this, we'll _____ all our money.
5 She was searching for the words that would _____ it _____.
6 The police are _____ on his story.
7 I started to _____ the drawers.
8 She hoped to _____ anything unpleasant that might be said.

Happening and creating

bring up   **come up**   **come up with**   **make up**   **think up**

I advised her to <u>bring</u> the matter <u>up</u>[1] at the next meeting.
I can't see you tonight. Something's <u>come up</u>[2].
She eventually <u>came up with</u> the compromise of an investigation by a committee of auditors.
He was a good storyteller, and used to <u>make up</u> tales about animals.
I kept <u>thinking up</u>[3] ways I could murder him without getting caught.

> ### LANGUAGE COMMENT
> [1] **Raise** means almost the same as **bring up**.
> [2] **Crop up** means almost the same as **come up**.
> [3] **Dream up** means almost the same as **think up**.

A *Using your understanding of the examples above, write the correct phrasal verb to complete the definitions. Be careful with verb forms.*

1 When you _____ _____ a particular subject, you mention it or introduce it into a discussion or conversation.
2 If you _____ _____ _____ a plan, idea, or solution, you think of it and suggest it.
3 If you _____ _____ a clever idea, you use your imagination or intelligence to create it.
4 If you _____ _____ something such as a story, you invent it, sometimes in order to deceive people.
5 When a problem, situation, or event _____ _____, it happens, perhaps unexpectedly.

B *Match the phrases on the left with those on the right.*

1 He was always boasting
2 Did you **come up with**

a   he tended to become evasive.
b   you can always get me on the phone.

3   If anything urgent **comes up**
4   Whenever she **brought up** the
    topic of money,
5   'Some suggestion,' he snorted.

c   and **making up** stories about where
    he'd been.
d   the right solutions to the dilemmas?
e   'Did you **think** this up all by yourself?'

1	2	3	4	5

C   *Write the correct form of the appropriate phrasal verb in the space provided.*

1   Whoever _____ this idea needs his head examined.
2   He's just _____ a story to get himself publicity for his autobiography.
3   I am sorry to _____ the subject of politics yet again.
4   A rather delicate assignment has _____.
5   I hope to _____ some of the answers.

Other meanings

look up   **make up**   **make up for**   **pick up**   **put up with**   **take up**   **turn up**

He consulted his dictionary to <u>look up</u> the meaning of the word 'apotheosis'.
Woman now <u>make up</u> two fifths of the British workforce.
She asked me about my interest, as if to <u>make up for</u> excluding me from the conversation.
Can you <u>pick up</u> the kids from school tonight? I've got a meeting.
I'm prepared to <u>put up with</u>[1] it for the time being.
She decided to <u>take up</u>[2] medicine as a career.
If it's a boring game the crowds won't <u>turn up</u>[3] next time.

LANGUAGE COMMENT
[1] **Endure** is a more formal word for **put up with**.
[2] **Go in for** means almost the same as **take up**.
[3] **Show up** means almost the same as **turn up**.

A   *Using your understanding of the examples above, write the correct phrasal verb to complete the definitions. Be careful with verb forms.*

1   To _____ _____ _____ something that is damaged, lost, or missing means to replace it or compensate for it.
2   If you _____ _____ a piece of information in a book, or on a timetable or map, you look there to find the information.
3   If you _____ _____ an activity or job, you start doing it.
4   If someone _____ _____, they arrive somewhere.
5   If you _____ _____ _____ something or someone, you tolerate or accept them, even though you find it difficult or unpleasant.
6   The people or things that _____ _____ something form that thing.
7   If you are driving a vehicle and you _____ someone or something _____, you stop the vehicle so that you can collect them and take them somewhere.

B   *Match the phrases on the left with those on the right.*

1   I **picked up** a hitchhiker
2   The service is terrible.
3   And why, at the age of thirty,
4   Lally said it would help me with my geography
5   Those who attended in the morning
6   Massive reductions in other areas would be required
7   Nearly half the Congress

a   he **took up** architecture, is not clear.
b   if I went and **looked** it **up** on a map.
c   I don't know how they **put up** with it.
d   **turned up** again for the afternoon session.
e   to **make up for** the expected shortfall in revenues.
f   on the way back from Zurich.
g   is **made up** of lawyers.

1	2	3	4	5	6	7

C   *Write the correct form of the appropriate phrasal verb in the space provided.*

1   You have to _____ these inconveniences as best you can.
2   Why don't you _____ the address in the directory?
3   A former vicar's wife has _____ belly dancing at the age of 71.
4   Young people from eighteen to thirty _____ a third of the Civil Defence force.
5   The next day, we _____ for work as usual.
6   The experience she gained in winning in Morocco will _____ the shortage of races in recent months.
7   Don't forget to _____ the clothes from the dry cleaner's.

Consolidation

Write a paragraph on one of the following topics, using at least six of the phrasal verbs you have studied in this unit.

a   The plan.
b   An apology.
c   New Year's Day.

More verbs with 'up'

Use the space below to record other verbs with 'up' you find in your studies. Write down the meaning in the second column and keep a note of the sentence in which you find the verb in the third column. An example is given.

UP – INCREASING AND IMPROVING		
do up	If you <u>do up</u> an old building, you repair it and decorate it and put in modern facilities.	You can make quite a lot of money <u>doing up</u> old properties.

UP – PREPARING		

UP – APPROACHING		

UP – DISRUPTING AND DAMAGING		

UP – COMPLETING AND FINISHING		

UP – HAPPENING AND CREATING		

UP – OTHER MEANINGS		

Shown below are seven more particles, each with one group of phrasal verbs.

Ahead	**Apart**	**Around/Round/About**
Making progress or thinking about the future	*Undoing or collapsing*	*Changing opinions, avoiding, and being inactive*
go ahead	fall apart	bring about
lie ahead	take apart	get around/round
plan ahead	tear apart	get around/round to
		stick around

By	**Forward**	**Through**	**Together**
Being prepared and surviving	*Looking to the future and presenting something*	*Completing and being thorough*	*Being in groups and organizing things*
get by	bring forward	fall through	get together
put by	look forward to	go through with	pull together
stand by	put forward	think through	put together

You can write other phrasal verbs with the same meaning in the space provided at the end of the unit. You can use a dictionary to help you.

Ahead

Making progress or thinking about the future

go ahead   **lie ahead**   **plan ahead**

The case will be discussed and he will be told whether or not he can go ahead[1].

Although the government has survived this challenge, others lie ahead.

They advised him to plan ahead[2] for an election.

LANGUAGE COMMENT

[1] **Proceed** is a more formal word for **go ahead**.
There is also a noun: *You have the go-ahead from the Prime Minister.*
There is also a related adjective: *...its go-ahead young secretary.*
Forge ahead, plough ahead, press ahead, and **push ahead** all have similar meanings.

[2] **Think ahead** means almost the same as **plan ahead**.

A   *Using your understanding of the examples above, write the correct phrasal verb to complete the definitions. Be careful with verb forms.*

1   If you _____ _____, you make arrangements in advance for something.

2   If an event or situation _____ _____, it is likely to happen in the future.

3   When someone _____ _____ with something which they planned, promised, or asked permission to do, they begin to do it.

B   *Match the phrases on the left with those on the right.*

1   The ballot   a   for whatever problems **lie ahead**.
2   He remains unprepared   b   will **go ahead** immediately.
3   Few individuals or families   c   **plan ahead** systematically.

1	2	3

C   *Write the correct form of the appropriate phrasal verb in the space provided.*

1   To be successful in business you have to _____ months or years
     _____.

2   Harder decisions _____.

3   They are _____ with the missile.

Apart

Undoing and collapsing

fall apart   **take apart**   **tear apart**

It is men who are more likely to <u>fall apart</u>[1] when their marriages break down.
Their tasks include <u>taking apart</u>[2] and reassembling large bits of furniture.
He was fighting against the 'anarchy' which he insisted was <u>tearing</u> the Church <u>apart</u>.

LANGUAGE COMMENT

[1] **Collapse** means almost the same as **fall apart**.
[2] **Dismantle** is a more formal word for **take apart**, and **put together** means the opposite.

A   *Using your understanding of the examples above, write the correct phrasal verb to complete the definitions. Be careful with verb forms.*

1   If something _____ a person, organization, or country _____, it
     causes them to experience great conflicts or disturbances.

2   If an organization, system, or relationship _____ _____ , it no longer
     works effectively and eventually fails or ends completely.

3   If you _____ something _____, you separate it into the different
     parts that it is made from.

B   *Match the phrases on the left with those on the right.*

1   They have lived through so much   a   to be cleaned.
     together;   b   what could possibly **tear** them
2   Most of these machines have to be   **apart**?
     taken apart   c   when the President refused to
3   The conference **fell apart**   participate.

1	2	3

53

C   *Write the correct form of the appropriate phrasal verb in the space provided.*

1   I'll have to _____ the bike _____.
2   Violence is _____ one of the world's big, if not great, cities.
3   Their marriage began to _____.

Around/Round/About

Changing opinions, avoiding, and being inactive

bring about   **get around/round**   **get around/round to**   **stick around**

The Administration helped <u>bring about</u> a peaceful settlement.
An impasse has developed and I don't know how to <u>get around</u>[1] it.
I didn't <u>get around to</u>[2] taking the examination.
Mike wanted me to <u>stick around</u>[3] for a couple of days.

> **LANGUAGE COMMENT**
>
> Note that in American English, **around** is much more common than **round**.
> [1] **Get round** means the same as **get around**.
> [2] **Get round to** means the same as **get around to**.
> [3] **Hang around** and **stay around** mean almost the same as **stick around**.

A   *Using your understanding of the examples above, write the correct phrasal verb to complete the definitions. Be careful with verb forms.*

1   To _____ something _____ means to cause it to happen.
2   If you _____ _____ or _____ _____ a difficulty or restriction, you find a way of avoiding it or of escaping its effects.
3   If you _____ _____, you stay where you are, often because you are waiting for something.
4   If you _____ _____ _____ or _____ _____ _____ doing something, you do it after a long delay because you were previously too busy or reluctant to do it.

B   *Match the phrases on the left with those on the right.*

1	I only **got around to**	a	should **get around** that clause.
2	I'll **stick around**	b	What had **brought** it **about**?
3	A good lawyer	c	and keep an eye on the food.
4	But why was all this happening?	d	doing the other things a few days ago.

1	2	3	4

54

C *Write the correct form of the appropriate phrasal verb in the space provided.*

1 There's nothing else to _____ for.
2 Naturally, one wonders what may have taken place to _____ the separation _____.
3 To help _____ this problem, some tanks are now equipped with radar.
4 It was only on the following day that they finally _____ interviewing Meehan.

By

Being prepared and surviving

get by   **put by**   **stand by**

You can <u>get by</u> in any English conversation with a very limited vocabulary.
You should start <u>putting</u> something <u>by</u>[1] for when the children are older.
Government engineers were <u>standing by</u>[2] to provide emergency repairs in the event of a breakdown.

LANGUAGE COMMENT

[1] **Put aside** and **set aside** mean almost the same as **put by**.
[2] There is also a noun: *...it is a good <u>standby</u> in an emergency.*

A *Using your understanding of the examples above, write the correct phrasal verb to complete the definitions. Be careful with verb forms.*

1 If you _____ _____ in a difficult situation, you manage to cope with it.
2 If you _____ _____, you are ready to provide help or take action if it becomes necessary.
3 If you _____ _____ a sum of money or a supply of something, you save it so that you can use it later.

B *Match the phrases on the left with those on the right.*

1 **Stand by** with lots of water   a to have something **put by**.
2 It's always a good idea   b in case a fire breaks out.
3 It's possible to **get by**   c in a job interview by just talking about your interests.

1	2	3

C *Write the correct form of the appropriate phrasal verb in the space provided.*

1 Although the budget's been cut again, we should just _____.
2 I'll be _____ in case of trouble, so don't worry.
3 With what he'd _____, he could live in luxury for the rest of his life.

Forward

Looking to the future and presenting something

bring forward   **look forward to**   **put forward**

Ask him to <u>bring</u> the meeting <u>forward</u>[1] to eight o'clock.
I'm quite <u>looking forward to</u> seeing Rick again.
Four civil engineering firms have <u>put forward</u>[2] plans for a new private motorway.

> **LANGUAGE COMMENT**
>
> [1] **Put forward** means almost the same as **bring forward,** and **put back** means the opposite.
> [2] **Propose** and **set out** mean almost the same as **put forward.**

A   *Using your understanding of the examples above, write the correct phrasal verb to complete the definitions. Be careful with verb forms.*

1   If you _____ _____ an idea or proposal, you state it or publish it so that people can consider it and discuss it.

2   If you _____ _____ _____ something that is going to happen, you want it to happen because you expect to enjoy it.

3   If you _____ _____ a meeting or an event, you arrange for it to be at an earlier time or date than was planned.

B   *Match the phrases on the left with those on the right.*

1   I did not **look forward**
2   Moscow said recently it would
3   The match would have

a   **to** my meeting with the manager.
b   **put forward** new proposals.
c   to be **brought forward**.

1	2	3

C   *Write the correct form of the appropriate phrasal verb in the space provided.*

1   The meeting has been _____ to Tuesday.

2   The idea was first _____ by J. Good.

3   I _____ leaving school next summer.

Through

Completing or being thorough

fall through   **go through with**   **think through**

But the scheme <u>fell through</u>, despite all my careful instructions.
The government was determined to <u>go through with</u> that legislation.
I haven't really <u>thought</u> the whole business <u>through</u> in my own mind.

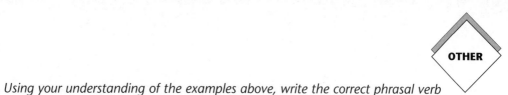

A   *Using your understanding of the examples above, write the correct phrasal verb to complete the definitions. Be careful with verb forms.*

1   If you _____ a situation _____, you consider it thoroughly, together with all its possible effects or consequences.

2   If an arrangement or plan _____ _____, something goes wrong with it before it can be completed and it has to be abandoned.

3   If you _____ _____ _____ a decision or an action, you continue to do what is necessary in order to achieve it or complete it.

B   *Match the phrases on the left with those on the right.*

1   I've been **thinking** it all **through**   a   and I do just want to see for myself.
2   When you start something,   b   you must **go through with** it.
3   Have a substitute scheme in mind   c   for a time when plans **fall through**.

1	2	3

C   *Write the correct form of the appropriate phrasal verb in the space provided.*

1   He tried to persuade me to change my mind, but I knew I had to _____ _____ it.

2   He also had plans for American publication, but it all _____.

3   It really needs to be _____ much more than this, before we proceed.

Together

Being in groups and organizing things

get together   pull together   put together

Do you think we could <u>get together</u>[1] at Christmas?

That's quite enough of that. <u>Pull</u> yourself <u>together</u> now and stop this at once.

The shipyards possess years of expertise in <u>putting together</u>[2] such big metal structures.

LANGUAGE COMMENT

[1] There is also a noun: *We're having a little <u>get-together</u> to celebrate Helen's promotion.*

[2] **Assemble** is a more formal word for **put together**, and **take apart** means the opposite.

A   *Using your understanding of the examples above, write the correct phrasal verb to complete the definitions. Be careful with verb forms.*

1   If you _____ _____ an object or its parts, you join its parts to each other so that it can be used.

2   When you _____ yourself _____, you control your feelings and behave calmly after you have been upset or angry.

3   When people _____ _____, they meet in order to discuss something or to spend time together.

B   *Match the phrases on the left with those on the right.*

1   He's a good player,   a   we **get together** for a drink sometime.
2   He suggested   b   but he needs to **pull** himself **together.**
3   The agency has **put together** c   the biggest ever campaign for a new car.

1	2	3

C   *Write the correct form of the appropriate phrasal verb in the space provided.*

1   Can you _____ with Henry to arrange the wedding reception?

2   He had taken some minutes alone in his room to _____ himself _____.

3   Grease the valve thoroughly and _____ the parts _____ again.

Consolidation

Write a paragraph on one of the following topics, using at least five of the phrasal verbs you have studied in this unit.

a   The future.
b   A camping trip.
c   Persuasion.

More verbs with other particles

Use the space below to record other verbs with these particles that you find in your studies. Write down the meaning in the second column and keep a note of the sentence in which you find the verb in the third column. An example is given.

AHEAD – MAKING PROGRESS OR THINKING ABOUT THE FUTURE		

APART – UNDOING OR COLLAPSING		

AROUND/ROUND/ABOUT – CHANGING OPINIONS, AVOIDING, AND BEING INACTIVE		

BY – BEING PREPARED AND SURVIVING		
drop by	To <u>drop by</u> means to visit someone without having arranged the visit.	If there's anything you want to see, just <u>drop by</u>.

FORWARD - LOOKING TO THE FUTURE AND PRESENTING SOMETHING		

THROUGH – COMPLETING AND BEING THOROUGH		

TOGETHER – BEING IN GROUPS AND ORGANIZING THINGS		

Key to Exercises

UNIT 1: AWAY
Withdrawing and separating

A	1	run away
	2	take away
	3	get away
	4	keep away
	5	give away
B	1	d
	2	e
	3	b
	4	a
	5	c
C	1	keep away
	2	give away
	3	ran away
	4	get away
	5	taken away

Other meanings

A	1	hide away
	2	fades away
	3	put away
	4	get away with
	5	throw away
B	1	c
	2	d
	3	b
	4	e
	5	a
C	1	hide away
	2	get away with
	3	faded away
	4	throw away
	5	put away

UNIT 2: BACK
Returning or repeating

A	1	take back
	2	call back
	3	give back
	4	get back
B	1	c
	2	d
	3	b
	4	a
C	1	take back
	2	get back
	3	call back
	4	gave back

Controlling or suppressing

A	1	cut back on
	2	sets back
	3	fight back
B	1	c
	2	b
	3	a
C	1	set back
	2	cut back on
	3	fight back

UNIT 3: DOWN
Decreasing and reducing

A	1	calms down
	2	play down
	3	cut down
	4	comes down
	5	bring down
	6	slows down; slow down
B	1	d
	2	b
	3	c
	4	f
	5	e
	6	a
C	1	come down
	2	bring down
	3	calmed down
	4	slowed down
	5	cut down
	6	play down

Defeating and suppressing

A	1	pull down
	2	back down
	3	put down
	4	knock down; knocks down
B	1	d
	2	a
	3	c
	4	b
C	1	puts down
	2	pull down
	3	backed down
	4	knocked down

Completing or failing

A	1	breaks down
	2	closes down
	3	turn down
	4	settle down
	5	let down
B	1	e
	2	c
	3	a
	4	b
	5	d
C	1	let down
	2	turned down
	3	breaks down
	4	settle down
	5	closed down

Writing and recording

A	1	take down
	2	put down to
	3	lay down
B	1	a
	2	b
	3	c
C	1	taking down
	2	laid down
	3	put down to

UNIT 4: IN
Inserting and absorbing

A
1. take in
2. sinks in
3. put in

B
1. b
2. c
3. a

C
1. took in
2. put in
3. sunk in

Being involved and active

A
1. fit in
2. join in
3. put in

B
1. b
2. c
3. a

C
1. putting in
2. joined in
3. fit in

Other meanings

A
1. give in
2. stay in
3. fill in

B
1. a
2. c
3. b

C
1. staying in
2. fill in
3. give in

UNIT 5: OFF
Leaving and beginning

A
1. see off
2. set off
3. drop off
4. takes off

B
1. c
2. d
3. a
4. b

C
1. taking off
2. see off
3. drop off
4. setting off

Rejecting and preventing

A
1. write off
2. put off
3. laid off

B
1. c
2. a
3. b

C
1. putting off
2. laid off
3. write off

Stopping, cancelling, and finishing

A
1. pull off
2. take off
3. finish off
4. call off
5. pay off

B
1. a
2. e
3. d
4. c
5. b

C
1. called off
2. finish off
3. take off
4. pull off
5. pay off

Other meanings

A
1. wears off
2. show off
3. goes off
4. tell off
5. goes off

B
1. b
2. c
3. d
4. e
5. a

C
1. gone off
2. wear off
3. told off
4. going off
5. showing off

UNIT 6: ON
Continuing and progressing

A
1. go on
2. getting on
3. get on
4. coming on
5. stay on
6. pass on

B
1. d
2. b
3. c
4. a
5. f
6. e

C
1. stay on
2. getting on
3. passed on
4. getting on
5. went on
6. gone on

Other meanings

A
1. going on
2. go on
3. take on
4. get on
5. move on to

B	1	e
	2	d
	3	a
	4	b
	5	c

C	1	go on
	2	move on to
	3	taken on
	4	going on
	5	get on with

UNIT 7: OUT
Leaving and beginning

A	1	take out
	2	set out
	3	breaks out
	4	go out

B	1	d
	2	c
	3	a
	4	b

C	1	broken out
	2	go out
	3	took out
	4	set out

Removing and excluding

A	1	keep out
	2	get out of
	3	talk out of
	4	cross out
	5	knock out
	6	leave out
	7	throw out

B	1	f
	2	g
	3	e
	4	a
	5	c
	6	d
	7	b

C	1	left out
	2	get out of
	3	crossed out
	4	knock out
	5	throw out
	6	keep out
	7	talk out of

Searching and finding

A	1	turns out
	2	make out
	3	check out
	4	try out
	5	find out

B	1	e
	2	c
	3	b
	4	d
	5	a

C	1	checked out
	2	turned out
	3	try out
	4	find out
	5	make out

Ending or disappearing

A	1	sold out
	2	run out; runs out
	3	wears out
	4	wipe out

B	1	b
	2	d
	3	c
	4	a

C	1	wipe out
	2	sold out
	3	run out
	4	wore out

Other meanings

A	1	look out
	2	give out
	3	fall out
	4	sort out
	5	carry out

B	1	c
	2	a
	3	b
	4	e
	5	d

C	1	fell out
	2	gave out
	3	carried out
	4	sorting out
	5	Look out

UNIT 8: OVER
Considering and communicating

A	1	put over
	2	talk over
	3	think over

B	1	a
	2	c
	3	b

C	1	put over
	2	talk over
	3	think over

Changing and transferring

A	1	take over
	2	win over
	3	take over

B	1	a
	2	b
	3	c

C	1	taken over
	2	winning over
	3	took over

Other meanings

A 1 runs over
2 get over with
3 get over

B 1 c
2 a
3 b

C 1 get over with
2 running over
3 get over

UNIT 9: UP
Increasing and improving

A 1 builds up; build up
2 cheer up; cheers up
3 save up
4 bring up
5 grow up
6 goes up
7 brush up

B 1 d
2 f
3 b
4 c
5 a
6 g
7 e

C 1 save up
2 brought up
3 gone up
4 brush up
5 grew up
6 build up
7 Cheer up

Preparing

A 1 set up/fix up
2 warm up
3 dress up
4 fix up/set up

B 1 b
2 a
3 d
4 c

C 1 set up
2 fixed up
3 dressed up
4 warm up

Approaching

A 1 face up to
2 lives up to
3 keep up
4 catch up

B 1 d
2 b
3 a
4 c

C 1 catching up
2 living up to
3 face up to
4 keep up

Disrupting and damaging

A 1 blow up; blows up
2 holds up
3 mess up
4 breaks up; break up
5 mix up

B 1 d
2 e
3 a
4 b
5 c

C 1 mess up
2 blown up
3 breaking up
4 mix up
5 holding up

Completing and finishing

A 1 do up
2 end up
3 use up
4 give up
5 sum up
6 check up
7 tidy up
8 cover up

B 1 g
2 f
3 e
4 c
5 h
6 b
7 a
8 d

C 1 gave up
2 ended up
3 did up
4 use up
5 sum up
6 checking up
7 tidy up
8 cover up

Happening and creating

A 1 bring up
2 come up with
3 think up
4 make up
5 comes up

B 1 c
2 d
3 b
4 a
5 e

C	1	thought up
	2	made up
	3	bring up
	4	come up
	5	come up with

Other meanings

A	1	make up for
	2	look up
	3	take up
	4	turns up
	5	put up with
	6	make up
	7	pick up

B	1	f
	2	c
	3	a
	4	b
	5	d
	6	e
	7	g

C	1	put up with
	2	look up
	3	taken up
	4	make up
	5	turned up
	6	make up for
	7	pick up

UNIT 10: OTHER PARTICLES
Ahead

A	1	plan ahead
	2	lies ahead
	3	goes ahead

B	1	b
	2	a
	3	c

C	1	plan ahead
	2	lie ahead
	3	going ahead

Apart

A	1	tears apart
	2	falls apart
	3	take apart

B	1	b
	2	a
	3	c

C	1	take apart
	2	tearing apart
	3	fall apart

Around/Round/About

A	1	bring about
	2	get around; get round
	3	stick around
	4	get around to; get round to

B	1	d
	2	c
	3	a
	4	b

C	1	stick around
	2	bring about
	3	get around/get round
	4	got around to/got round to

By

A	1	get by
	2	stand by
	3	put by

B	1	b
	2	a
	3	c

C	1	get by
	2	standing by
	3	put by

Forward

A	1	put forward
	2	look forward to
	3	bring forward

B	1	a
	2	b
	3	c

C	1	brought forward
	2	put forward
	3	look forward to

Through

A	1	think through
	2	falls through
	3	go through with

B	1	a
	2	b
	3	c

C	1	go through with
	2	fell through
	3	thought through

Together

A	1	put together
	2	pull together
	3	get together

B	1	b
	2	a
	3	c

C	1	get together
	2	pull together
	3	put together